BLACK SCIENTISTS & INVENTORS

BOOK 1

Ava Henry
And
Michael Williams

Black Scientists & Inventors Book 1

Written by: **Ava Henry and Michael Williams**
Researched by: **Ava Henry and Michael Williams**
Consulting Publishers: **Andrew Williams, Patrick Williams**
Layout and Design: **Jeorge Asare-Djan**
Illustrations: **Jeorge Asare-Djan, Wamakuta Zikomo,**
Illustrations coloured by: **Jeorge Asare-Djan**

Published by: BIS Publications LTD

Tel: 0845 226 4066
web: www.bispublications.com
email: info@bispublications.com
First Published: 2003
ISBN: 1-903289-00-9

BIS Publications PO BOX 14918 London N17 8WJ

First Printed in 1999
Second Printing in 2002
Third Printing in 2005
Fourth Printing in 2007
Fifth Printing in 2010

A catalogue record for this book exists in the British Library.

Contents

Acknowledgements

I would sincerely like to thank all of the children: Davina Quinland,
Suzanna & Danielle Williams, Duro & Ore Howell, Shanike Howell, Shani Zikomo
and their parents, Yolanda James, Derek & Marion Williams, Jennifer and
Wendy Howell, Wamakuta Zikomo who helped to review and test the questions
and made useful comments and those who helped with the editing and
general educational direction of the book, Tema Mwangi, Mike,
Patrick and Andrew Williams. I would also like to thank the children of
the Mosiah Foundation/Sankofa School, for helping with the concept of producing
a book of black scientists and inventors. Your help was invaluable in the
production of this book. I hope you can all lend a hand for the upcoming editions.

Ava Henry & Michael Williams.

Instructions

This book is designed to be used by children between the ages of 7 - 16. It covers the topic of Black Scientists and Inventors. It contains biographies of notable black scientists and inventors from the UK, America, the Caribbean and Africa, questions on the biographies, extra activity based questions, an answer section, a Timeline of Scientists, Inventors & Inventions, Glossary and a Bibliography for further reading.

This book will help pupils to develop their reading, comprehension, maths, history and science skills. It is the authors' hope that parents and teachers will help the children on this journey of knowledge and discovery.

Extra Questions
These questions are ideas for mini-projects or essay topics. Ask your teacher, parent, older brother/sister or relative for help.

Timeline
This is a timeline of Scientists, Inventors and Inventions useful for history projects.

Glossary
This contains explanations of some of the words and phrases used in the biographies. This can be used in place of specialist dictionaries where necessary.

Answers
(Special note to students)
The answers to the questions are in the Answers section of the book. However, they are there as a guide, use them only after you have looked in the dictionary, the encyclopædia, searched the internet and have been to the library. Please attempt all the questions before looking at the answers. Do not be disappointed if you get some of the answers wrong, remember this is a learning exercise. It is more important that you learn about the scientists and inventors and key facts in the book, so that you can be inspired to do great things in your life. Remember if you cheat, you will only be cheating yourself. Good Luck and have fun while learning!

Bibliography
We have also included a bibliography and catalogue for further reading. Please contact us if you need to purchase any of the items listed.

Note to Parents and Teachers
The biographies are only a guide. Any additional information that you have about any of the scientists/inventors, can be used to embellish the material. Do suggest resources such as the library, relevant websites and dictionaries that the children can use. Do set mini-projects where you can. Do have fun!

Madam C.J Walker
(1867 - 1919)

Madam C.J Walker was born Sarah Breedlove on December 23rd, 1867 in Delta, Louisiana, USA. Her parents were ex-slaves who had become sharecroppers on their ex-master's farm. She was the youngest of three children. At the age of seven, her parents died from yellow fever. This was a time in America's history where the country was very much segregated into black and white. There were very little prospects for employment or education for black people unless they set up those institutions for themselves.

Her brother left home to find work and after they lost the farm, Madam C.J Walker and her sister went to work as laundry assistants. She got married at the age of fourteen to Moses Macmillan with whom she had a child.

In 1887 at the age of twenty, her husband was killed in an accident. Madam C.J Walker then moved to St. Louis where she married John Davis and worked for a black-owned hair-care company called Poro Co. After this unsuccessful marriage Madam C.J Walker moved to Denver to live with her brother's family. She was employed as a cook and after noticing that her hair had begun to fall out, she began experimenting with products of her own to remedy her situation.

One night she dreamt of a black man, who told her where to go to source the right ingredients for a hair growing solution. Madam C.J Walker, with the help of family and friends produced **Wonderful Hair Grower**™, **Vegetable Shampoo**™ and **Glossine**™ after months of rigorous trials. She later invented a hot-comb.

Madam C.J Walker became a door-to-door sales agent for her products. This financed her newspaper advertisements, which brought in mail orders for her products. In 1906, Madam C.J Walker married Charles Joseph Walker, who was a sales man for a black-owned newspaper, she later adopted his name. They expanded the product lines and employed staff who shared in the profits from the sales. The demand for the products grew rapidly. Madam C.J Walker opened schools and colleges in cities across America and the Caribbean to train women with her hair-care products.

Although Madam C.J Walker could not read until later on in her life, she became the first African American woman millionaire in America. She was also a caring and compassionate woman. She donated $10,000 to young black men and women to further their education and sponsored six students to attend the black-run Tuskegee Institute.

"…My object in life is not simply to make money for myself or to spend it on myself. I love to use part of what I make in trying to help others…"

Madam C.J Walker
Questions

1. In what year did Madam C.J Walker's parents die and what did they die of?

2. What is a sharecropper?

3. What products did Madam C.J Walker invent?

4. How did Madam C.J Walker come to invent her solutions?

5. How did Madam C.J Walker help other people?

Extra Questions

1. How did Madam C.J Walker let people know about her inventions?
2. What are advertisements?
3. What is an entrepreneur?
4. How was Madam C.J Walker an entrepreneur?

Habitats

Worms, Squirrels and Wood lice. Where do they live (What is their habitat)?
clue: try your local park. How do they feed? Why do they look and act they way they do?
Do they have feet, claws, how do they move, how do they sleep?

What you will need:
A friend or an older brother or sister or a parent to accompany you, pen and paper.

Method:
Copy the questions above. Visit your school library or search the internet to find the answers to the questions above or when you are in the park, find a Ranger and ask him/her the questions.

Results:
Write a table of your results like the one below: (you may need to turn your paper length-wise to landscape to fit all the columns)

Subject	Habitat	Feed by	Reason for looks & actions	Feet / Claws	How do they Move?	How do they Sleep?
Worms						
Squirrels						
Wood Lice						

INVENTOR

SCIENTIST

HISTORICAL FIGURE

ANSWERS

GLOSSARY

TIMELINE

Ron Headley
(1939)

Ron Headley was born on June 29th 1939 in Kingston, Jamaica. This was also the year that Word War II began. He spent his early years in Kingston and at the age of 13 he moved to England. Ron played cricket for Worcestershire and like his father Sir George Headley, played internationally for the West Indies.

When the cricket season was over Ron worked as a car salesman in the West Midlands, England. It was during these times that he would work on his invention, which has now become known as the **Ecocharger**™.

The **Ecocharger**™ is a "cleaner diesel engine emission system". It improves the performance of diesel cars because it reduces smoke emission, fuel consumption and allows cars to run for 150,000 miles without major maintenance. Ron's innovation succeeds where others fail. It "...works on the fuel before combustion, so there is no need for a catalytic converter to clean up the exhaust afterwards." This allows us all to breathe cleaner air.

Headley is a man known for his simple but effective ideas. He was awarded a British patent for the **Ecocharger**™ innovation in 1985. His son Dean Headley played international cricket for England. Ron lives in Birmingham with his wife.

"...The best inventions rely on simplicity...".

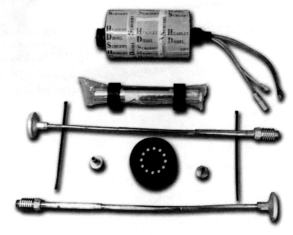

The Ecocharger ™

Ron Headley
Questions

1. What year was Ron Headley born and what other significant event occurred in that year?

2. When did Ron Headley move to England?

3. How old is Ron Headley?

4. What sport is Ron Headley well known for and what did he do when his sporting season was over?

5. What did Ron Headley invent and how does it work?

6. When and where was Ron Headley awarded a patent for the Ecocharger™?

Extra Questions

1. What is combustion? Explain.
2. What is a catalytic converter?
3. What is the difference between the Ecocharger™ and a catalytic converter?
4. Do you find it unusual that a cricketer can also be a car salesman as well as an inventor?

Magic Salt

What you will need:
A tablespoon, salt , a ruler, 2 half-filled glasses or beakers of water. A safe, warm place to rest the glasses or beakers, on a window sill over a radiator, on the side in the kitchen, a ruler.

Method:
Pour a table spoon of salt in one beaker, stir until it dissolves, or until you can no longer see it. Place the beakers in a warm place for 4 hours. Measure the water level of both beakers once every hour, record your results. Leave beakers overnight (10 hours). Measure the water levels. What has changed? Record your results. Write about why you think the changes have happened.

Results:

Solution	Water Level after 1 hour	Water Level after 2 hours	Water Level after 3 hours	Water Level after 4 hours	Water Level after 10 hours
Plain Water					
Salty Water					

Benjamin Banneker
(1731 - 1806)

Benjamin Banneker was born on November 9th 1731 in Maryland, USA to parents who were free citizens. During this time many African American people were slaves and were not allowed to attend school. Banneker was taught to read and write by his grandmother. As a child he liked maths, puzzles and games, he also liked to lie on his back and gaze at the stars in amazement. He did this so often that his neighbours gave him the nickname "the stargazer".

When he left school, he went to work on his father's farm. He decided to make his farm life his new classroom. He studied the plants, the animals and the weather. By the age of 20, he had mastered many of the key concepts in mathematics, science and philosophy without receiving any formal qualifications.

At the age of 22, Banneker invented **a clock that he carved out of wood by hand.** The clock was the first of its kind in America and kept good time for over 50 years. Banneker befriended a local businessman, George Ellicot. After observing how passionate Banneker was, Ellicot lent him books on mathematics and astronomy. By 1789, Banneker had accumulated so much knowledge in the field of astronomy that he predicted a solar eclipse. In 1771 Banneker was one of the surveyors who **laid out the plans for Washington DC**, which later became the capital city of the USA. Banneker published his first almanac in 1792. This was a book that included information about the weather, planets, stars, a calendar, medical remedies, poems and articles demanding the abolition of slavery.

Through his life experiences, Benjamin Banneker illustrated that education neither begins nor ends at school. We should always endeavour to find out about the world in which we live. We should also view every experience, regardless of how negative it may seem, as an opportunity to learn something new about ourselves and life in general.

Here are ways to broaden your horizons:

Go to the **library**, use the **Internet**, use **educational CDs** to **research** your favourite subject, game or hobby.

Go to **exhibitions, museums** and **ask your teachers** questions about how that subject area has developed over the years.

Talk to friends and relatives about a variety of topics, perhaps the daily news coverage.

Read the local, national and specialist newspapers. These can be read in the library.

Start to **build your own library** at home by buying books, magazines and by keeping cuttings books and journals.

Benjamin Banneker
Questions

INVENTOR

1. What nickname did Benjamin's neighbours give to him and why?

2. What did he do after he left school and how did he master his new job?

SCIENTIST

3. What did Benjamin Banneker invent and how old was he?

4. What was special about his invention?

HISTORICAL FIGURE

5. What event occurred in 1789 that was predicted by Benjamin Banneker?

6. What important contribution did Benjamin Banneker make to the USA?

Extra Questions

ANSWERS

1. What is an almanac? (Go to the library to get some names of almanacs.)

2. What is a solar eclipse? (Find out about the dates of past solar eclipses and the next predicted ones.)

3. Did you see the solar eclipse on August 11th 1999? Where in the world were you when it took place?

4. What is a surveyor?

5. What lessons does Benjamin Banneker's life experiences teach us? (Ask your teacher or your parents to show you an example of a cuttings book and an example of a journal.)

GLOSSARY

TIMELINE

Granville T. Woods
(1856 - 1910)

Many national newspapers across America in the 1880s described him as the greatest electrician that ever lived. Granville T. Woods was born in Ohio, USA on 23rd April 1856. He was the son of Tailer and Martha Woods.

Granville left school when he was ten years old and worked in a machine shop. He had many different jobs such as a fireman in a railroad company. He worked in a machine shop during the day and studied electricity at night school.

In 1884 at the age of 28, Woods began his career as one of Americas most talented inventors. His first invention was **an improvement to steam boiler furnaces.** This enabled the furnaces to heat homes and buildings better. Woods invented a new **telephone transmitter** that improved the distance and quality that sound could be sent, the American Bell Telephone company bought the patent from him. He invented a **special set of tracks** for motor cars to run on in amusement parks.

Woods held over 35 patents on electromechanical devices including an **incubator**. He is best known for his pioneering work in improving the railway system. He invented the **railway telegraphy system** used to communicate messages from one train to another.

In 1888 Woods invented an **overhead electric system** to power trains. This system replaced the steam engine powered trains with trains that were much cleaner to the environment. Trains are still powered with the overhead electric system. Woods also invented the **third rail** which runs along-side a rail track providing the trains with electrical power. These inventions are still used today to communicate and power trains and tube systems up and down many countries in the world.

Incidentally, Thomas Edison and Phelps accused Woods of infringement on several occasions because their company was working on a similar device. In two patent cases (Wood's Vs Phelps) Woods was twice declared the true inventor. Ironically, after their defeat, Edison and Phelps invited Woods to join their company. He declined the offer and established the Woods' Electrical Company where he worked with his brother Lyates Woods also an inventor.

In 1974 the governor of Ohio issued a proclamation to recognise Granville T. Woods as one of the greatest electricians in the world.

Granville T. Woods
Questions

1. When and where was Granville T. Woods born? What age did he leave school?

2. How did Granville T. Woods learn about electricity?

3. What did Granville T. Woods invent?

4. How many patents did Granville T. Woods hold?

5. Who did Granville T. Woods go to court with and what was he contesting?

6. What was the outcome of the court cases?

7. What happened after the court cases?

8. What special proclamation was made about Granville T. Woods, who made it and when was it made?

Extra Questions

1. What is an incubator?
2. What is Granville T. Woods 'third rail' used for today?
3. If Granville T. Woods had over 35 patents what does this say about how he worked?
4. After reading about Granville T. Woods life, what lessons have you learned?

Making Music

What you will need:
4 empty glass milk bottles, water, a ruler, 4 labels, pen and paper.

Method:
Label the bottles 3cm, 6cm, 9cm, 12cm, measure out as much water to pour into the bottles. Bring each bottle to your mouth and blow across the top. Describe the sound you hear. Record your results. Does the sound change for the different amounts of water? Why do you think this is?

Results:

Amount of Water in Bottle	Description of Sound
3cm	
6cm	
Etc	

INVENTOR

SCIENTIST

HISTORICAL FIGURE

ANSWERS

GLOSSARY

TIMELINE

Dr. Mae C. Jemison
(1956)

Dr. Jemison is an African American who was born on October 17th 1956 in Decatur, Alabama. She was raised in Chicago where she spent most of her childhood and teenage years. At the age of 16, she attended Stanford University on a scholarship and graduated with a Bachelor of Science (BSc) degree in Chemical Engineering and fulfilled the requirements for a Bachelor of Arts (BA) degree in African/Afro American studies. It was here that she developed an interest in biomedical engineering. She then attended Cornell University Medical College where she earned her doctorate in medicine (M.D).

Prior to joining the National Aeronautics and Space Administration (NASA) in 1987, Dr. Jemison worked in both engineering and medicine. She travelled widely. Dr. Jemison spent two and a half years as the Area Peace Corps medical officer for Sierra Leone and Liberia in West Africa (1983 - 1985) and was a Peace Corps volunteer in Cambodia. On her return, she worked as a General Practitioner (GP) in Los Angeles, USA, while updating her engineering skills.

At the age of 31, Dr. Jemison had the honour of being selected from over 2000 applicants to participate in an astronaut-training program at NASA, USA. On September 12th 1992, she became the first woman of colour to go into space aboard the space shuttle Endeavor. She spent a total of 190 hours, 30 minutes and 23 seconds in space. Dr. Jemison resigned from NASA in March 1993.

Dr. Jemison's current work focuses on the beneficial integration of science and technology into daily life. She founded the Jemison Group Inc., a small company that assesses the worldwide social and technological circumstances of users of new technology. Dr. Jemison also established a number of projects including, The Earth We Share™ (TEWS), an international science camp for young people, that is designed to build critical thinking and problem solving skills through an experiential curriculum. As director of the Jemison Institute for Advancing Technology in Developing Countries and Professor of Environmental Studies at Dartmouth College in the USA, Dr. Jemison works on sustainable development. This means she assesses methods that improve the quality of human life now, such that future generations can grow and prosper.

Dr. Jemison is a noted lecturer and has received many honours and awards, including the Essence Science and Technology Award and the Kilby Science Award. She was inducted into the National Woman's Hall of Fame and the National Medical Association Hall of Fame and has received numerous honorary doctorates. Dr. Jemison's hobbies include dancing and reading. She lives in Houston, Texas with her cat Little Mama.

Dr. Mae C. Jemison
Questions

1. When and where was Dr. Jemison born?

2. How many degrees does Dr. Jemison hold? Name them.

INVENTOR

3. Where in the world has Dr. Jemison's medical work taken her?

4. Name the projects Dr. Jemison currently works on and what are the aims of these projects?

SCIENTIST

5. What honours and awards have Dr. Jemison received?

6. Was Dr. Jemison the first woman of colour in space? If Yes, what was the name of the shuttle and when did it take off?

7. Does Dr. Jemison still work for NASA?

8. What does the phrase 'sustainable development' mean?

HISTORICAL FIGURE

Extra Questions

1. Dr. Jemison spent a total of 190 hours, 30 minutes and 23 seconds in space. Workout the total number of: seconds, minutes, hours, whole days, whole weeks, whole months.
2. What is space? (Find out about the solar system).
3. What is an astronaut?
4. What is meant by the word experiential?

ANSWERS

Heated Hands and Friction

What You Will Need:
Your two hands, a stopwatch or stop clock.

Method:
Make sure that your hands are dry. Only start the investigation when both of your hands are cold or cool. Clasp both hands together, then twist them up and down, repeat this for about 60 seconds.

GLOSSARY

Results:
What happens to the temperature of your hands and why?
What is friction?

TIMELINE

Elijah McCoy
(1843 - 1929)

Elijah McCoy was born in Colchester Ontario, Canada, on May 2nd 1843, to George and Emillia McCoy, who were both former slaves who had escaped slavery on the 'underground railroad'. The 'underground railroad' is a term used to describe a large network of people who helped slaves in the Southern States in America to escape to the Northern States or Canada where they would be free. Emillia and George knew it was illegal for slaves to learn how to read and write in the USA. They had high hopes for their 12 children, who would grow up as free individuals in their new country, Canada. Elijah's parents wanted to instil pride in their children and told them how fortunate they were to be able to get an education. From a young age Elijah was especially interested in mechanical devices.

At 16 his parents saved money for him to leave Canada and go to school in Edinburgh, Scotland to master drafting and engineering. He finished his studies and returned to Canada, but could not get work because of his race. He then left Canada to look for work in Detroit, Michigan. He eventually got work not as an engineer but as labourer on the railroad. He was in charge of oiling machinery. McCoy was intrigued by the way the machinery would grind to a halt when the parts needed oiling.

In 1870 he set up the Elijah McCoy Manufacturing Company in Detroit Michigan to work on a solution to stop machinery from grinding to a halt when the parts need oiling. In 1872 he invented the **drip cup** for oiling factory machinery, he later went on to invent the **lubricator cup** for the railroads. He had over 50 patents, including an **ironing table** and a **lawn sprinkler.**

Ever wondered where the phrase "the Real McCoy" really came from? Other inventors would copy McCoy's inventions and try to pass them off as their own. When they tried to sell the replica to manufacturing companies, the company would realise it did not work as good as McCoy's inventions so they would often ask, "Is this the Real McCoy?"

Elijah McCoy's legacy to international technology and innovation remains with us today. One only needs to look at naval boats, mining and construction machinery and space exploration vehicles to see variations of McCoy's **drip cup.**

McCoy strongly encouraged young children to Work Hard, Study and Think. He was undoubtedly THE REAL McCOY.

Elijah McCoy
Questions

1. When and where was Elijah McCoy born?

2. Why was it important for Elijah, his brothers and sisters to go to school?

3. What subject did Elijah McCoy become a master in?

4. When did he set up his company, what was it called and where was it located?

5. Why did he set up a company?

6. What did Elijah McCoy invent and how many patents did he have altogether?

Extra Questions

1. Why do you think Elijah McCoy's parents wanted to "instil pride" into their children?
2. Why is it important to learn to read and write?
3. Do all people know how to read and write?
4. What does it mean to become a master of something? What subject would you like to become a master of and why?
5. What do you think Elijah McCoy meant by "…work hard, study and think"?

Opposites Attract

What You Will Need:
Two rectangular shaped magnets, a clear flat surface such as a table top, a ruler.

Method:
Place the two magnets on the table about 10cm apart from each other with the two long ends opposite each other. Slowly move the magnets closer to each other until they meet. Now move the magnets to their original positions and turn one of them clockwise 180 degrees. Once again move the magnets slowly together until they meet.

Results:
What happened as they moved closer?
A magnet has two poles, what are the names of the poles:
North, East, South, or West?

INVENTOR

SCIENTIST

HISTORICAL FIGURE

ANSWERS

GLOSSARY

TIMELINE

Jan Ernst Matzeliger
(1852 - 1889)

Jan Ernst Matzeliger, was born on September 15th 1852 in Suriname, (Dutch Guyana) "and made shoes to last". This was a time when most people could not buy shoes because it took a long time to make each pair. Matzeliger changed that. He invented a machine that made shoes quickly and cheaply.

When Jan was a boy he worked in his father's mechanical workshop. Here, Jan learned how to use the lathe machine. At the age of 19, Jan became a seaman. He sailed to the Far East and then two years later sailed to Philadelphia in the USA, there Jan tried to find a job as a machine operator. However every machine shop he went to turned him away. Slavery had ended ten years earlier, but many whites did not respect blacks enough to employ them. He did not give up and was eventually hired by a shoemaker.

In 1877, Jan moved to Lynn, Massachusetts, the "shoe industry capital of the world" as it was affectionately known by workers in that area. Jan was hired at the Harney Brothers Shoe Factory. Jan liked the different machines: some cut and sewed the upper parts of the shoes whilst others attached the upper parts of the shoes to the sole. The most difficult part of shoemaking was connecting the upper part to the innersole. This is called **Lasting**. It had to be done by hand. The leather had to be stretched over a wooden model of the foot called a **last**. Then the finished shape had to be tacked into place onto the sole. There was no machine to do this work. Jan decided that he was going to invent such a machine.

People laughed when they heard Jan was trying to make a machine that could last shoes. Other workers had tried and failed. Nearly three years later Jan, had made **the lasting machine** from scrap metal. The machine lasted shoes perfectly. Jan had done what others had said was impossible. Another inventor offered to buy Jan's invention for $1,500, but he rejected the offer.

On March 20th 1883, Jan was given a patent from the US government for his lasting machine. Jan's invention could last from 300 to 700 pairs of shoes in a ten-hour workday. One person doing the same work by hand could finish 50 pairs of shoes in that time. Jan did not have enough money to fulfil the large number of orders for his **lasting machine**. A large company called the Consolidated Hand Method Lasting Machine Co., bought Jan's business. Jan's invention made many people rich, but he was left poor and almost forgotten. Jan Matzeliger added 37 more patents to his list of inventions during his life. In 1992, the US Government printed a special postage stamp to honour this great inventor.

Jan Matzeliger did not depend on others to share his vision. He showed us that living by example and possessing a strong determination to see through the bad times earned him respect in the end.

Shoe-lasting machine

Jan Ernst Matzeliger
Questions

1. When and where was Jan Ernst Matzeliger born?

2. What did Matzeliger invent, what was special about this invention and when did he receive a patent for it?

3. What did Matzeliger do at the age of 19 and where did it take him?

4. After his post, did he have problems getting a job? If Yes, why?

5. What did Matzeliger's colleagues think about his invention?

6. How did Matzeliger's invention compare with other lasting methods of the time?

   (Remember, his machine could last 300 to 700 pairs of shoes in a 10-hour day.

   By hand only 50 pairs of shoes could be lasted in the same period).

Extra Questions

1. Where is Suriname?
2. What is a lathe machine?
3. What do you think it would be like in a world without shoes?
   Think of what it would be like to live in a cold climate without shoes.
4. What lessons can we learn form Jan Ernst Matzeliger's life?

Shadows In The Night

What You Will Need:
A dark room with at least one clear wall, a torch and any safe object such as a toy, a shoe, a bat or even your own hand, a friend to help you. A ruler or tape measure, pen and paper.

Method:
Make sure that the only light on in the dark room is the torch. Ask your friend to hold the object up about 6 feet away from the wall in the room. Now point the torch in the direction of the object. Then slowly, move the object closer to the wall until you are 1 feet way from the wall, then slowly move the object back to the original position.

Results:
What do you see on the wall and why do you think this is?
What happened when you moved the object closer do the wall?
What would happen to your investigation if the torch was turned off?
What would happen if daylight was allowed into the room?

Distance	Description of Shadow
6 Feet	
4 Feet	
2 Feet	

Dr. Ernest Everett Just
(1883 - 1941)

Dr. Ernest Everett Just was born in South Carolina, USA on August 14th, 1883 to Charles Frazier and Mary Matthews Just. Ernest went to Kimball Hall Academy School in New Hampshire where he completed a four-year course of study in only three years. He then went on to study at Dartmouth College. At Dartmouth College Dr. Just won special honours in botany, sociology and history. In 1907 he was the only student to graduate from Dartmouth College as magna cum laude, or with a distinction.

In 1909 Dr. Just began to teach at Howard University and was also a research assistant for Professor Frank Rattray Lillie. In 1916, Dr. Just received the Degree of Doctor of Philosophy magna cum laude or with a distinction, from the University of Chicago. He had specialised in experimental embryology, with a thesis on the Mechanics of Fertilisation.

Dr. Just went on to advance science in many ways. His contributions were his incredible study into egg fertilisation and cellular research. In 1914, the National Association for the Advancement of Coloured People (NAACP) awarded Dr. Just with the Springarn Medal for his contribution to science and help to his race. In 1930, he was the first black vice-president of the American Society of Zoologists.

Dr. Just also wrote many papers on his research work, which included General Cytology, published in 1924 and he also contributed to volume two of Dr. Jerome Alexander's three-volume series on colloid chemistry. In 1924 Dr. Just was selected from among eminent biologists of the world by a group of German biologists to contribute to a monograph on fertilisation.

Through Dr. Just's diligent work the entire human family including animals have gained from his research on how the cells that are the building blocks of our bodies, work.

Dr. Ernest Everett Just
Questions

1. Where and when was Dr. Just born? What were the names of his parents?

2. What was special about the way Dr. Just completed his study at Kimball Hall Academy school?

3. What subjects did Dr. Just win special honours for at Dartmouth College?

4. When did Dr. Just graduate from Dartmouth College.

5. What was special about Dr. Just's graduation?

6. Which degree did Dr. Just receive at Chicago University and when?

7. How did Dr. Just contribute to the study of embryology?

8. What notable achievements did Dr. Just make?

Extra Questions

1. What is embryology?
2. In 1924 Dr. Just was selected by a team of German biologists to contribute to a monograph on fertilisation. What is a monograph?
3. Why is the study of how humans and animals develop in the early stages important?

Acidity

Testing the acidity (pH) of everyday substances:

What you will need:
You will need universal indicator paper, ask your teacher/parent/carer to get this for you. Orange juice, milk, water, tea, kitchen cleaner, toothpaste, face cream, washing up liquid. A stopwatch or stop-clock to time 1 minute for each test. Pen and paper.

Tip a universal indicator paper in each substance for 1 minute, record your results. What do you think makes these substances, alkaline, neutral or acidic?

Results:

Substance	Acidity (pH)
Orange juice	
Milk	
Etc	

INVENTOR
SCIENTIST
HISTORICAL FIGURE
ANSWERS
GLOSSARY
TIMELINE

Garrett A. Morgan
(1877 - 1963)

On March 4th 1877 Garrett A. Morgan an African American inventor was born in, Kentucky, USA to Sidney and Elizabeth Morgan. He only had an elementary school education, but was very smart. He was the seventh child of eleven brothers and sisters. When Morgan was in his teens he got a job as a sewing machine technician. Whilst in this job he invented a **belt fastener** for sewing machines. He sold this invention in 1901 for less than $50.00.

This invention inspired him to set up a business in the clothing industry. In 1909 Morgan opened a tailor shop with 32 workers in Cleveland, Ohio.

Morgan invented the first **gas mask** in 1912 and was given a patent for it by the US government. A patent is an official document used to prove that a person has invented or is allowed to sell a product. On July 25th 1916 in Cleveland, Ohio Garrett's mask was put to a real test when an explosion in a tunnel occurred. Over thirty men were trapped in the tunnel. There was no way of rescuing these men because of the gas and smoke. Morgan and his brother Frank heard what had happened and rushed into the tunnel wearing their gas masks. They rescued the men and news about the mask spread throughout the USA and the world.

Morgan set up a company where he manufactured his mask. He received very large contracts from all around the country to supply his gas mask to fire departments, mining companies and US army soldiers during World War I. Unfortunately his orders reduced when his customers found out that he was of African decent. In order to fool his customers Morgan would often use another product he invented in 1912 the **hair straightening cream** on himself, so as to pass as a full-blooded Indian from the Walpole Reservation in Canada.

In 1923, Garrett Morgan received a patent for another life saving invention, the **traffic signalling system.** Before his invention there were many street accidents. The three-colour electric traffic signal can now be seen in practically every city in the world. Some years later, Morgan sold the rights for his signalling system to the General Electric Corporation (GEC) for $40,000; this may have been an attempt to conceal his identity.

Garrett A. Morgan died in 1963 at the age of 86.

Garrett A. Morgan
Questions

1. When was Garrett Morgan born and what education did he receive?

2. What was Garrett Morgan's first invention and how old was he when he invented it?

3. What is a patent? (Give examples.)

4. What was Garrett Morgan's second invention and when did he receive a patent for it?

5. When was Garrett Morgan's second invention put to the test and where was this invention used?

6. What else did Garrett Morgan invent and when?

Extra Questions

1. What do you think your high street would be like without traffic lights? Explain.
2. Why did Garrett Morgan experience problems in selling his inventions and how did he get around these problems? (Why do you think he did what he did?)

Light Sources

Can you name three natural sources of light?
Name two natural sources of light which also produce heat?
Can you name two unnatural sources of light and do they produce heat?

What you will need:
A torch, a stopwatch or stop-clock.

Method:
Get a torch, switch it on for 5 minutes then switch it off. Without touching the torch, put your hands close to it. Is it warm or cold? Why is it the temperature it is?

Space:
Can you name all the planets in our solar system? How many moons move around the planet earth? What gas on earth do we need to breathe? What is the main gas on the Sun?
Is there gravity on the moon?

If its June 21st and 5pm GMT (Greenwich Mean Time) in England what are the times in Hong Kong, Australia, Ghana, Cuba, India, Germany, Fiji, New York and California? Write your results in a table of Time against Countries/City like the one below:

Times	Country/City
5.00PM	England
	Hong Kong
	Etc.

Answers

Only look at the answers in each section when you have attempted all the questions in that section. Remember you can only cheat yourself.

To get additional help to answer extra questions please visit www.bispublications.com/blackscientistsbook1

Madam C.J Walker

1. 1874. Yellow fever is a viral disease carried by mosquitoes. The symptoms of yellow fever begin to appear 9 - 12 days after receiving a bite from a mosquito carrier. The virus damages the liver and causes a yellowish bile pigment to gather in the skin. Other symptoms of the disease are fever, headaches, dizziness and muscle ache.

2. A person most likely an ex-slave who owns a share of a landlord's land.

3. Hair grower solutions, hot-comb.

4. She lost her hair, experimented with various products and saw the ingredients in a dream.

5. She sponsored disadvantaged children to finish their education. She employed lots of black women in her factories and schools.

Ron Headley

1. 1939, World War II.

2. 1952.

3. Subtract 1939 from the current year.

4. Cricket. He worked as a car salesman.

5. The Ecocharger. It alters the fuel before combustion so that less dangerous gases are emitted into the environment.

6. 1985, Britain.

Benjamin Banneker

1. "the stargazer". As a boy, he used to lie on his back and gaze at the stars for hours.

2. He went to work on his father's farm and decided that the farm would be his new classroom; he studied the plants, animals and weather.

3. A hand-carved wooden clock. 22.

4. The clock kept good time for over 50 years and it was the first of its kind in America.

5. A solar eclipse.

6. He was one of the surveyors who laid out the plans for Washington D.C, which later became the capital city of the USA. His hand-carved wooden clock was also an important contribution the USA.

Granville T. Woods

1. April 23rd 1856 in Ohio, USA. 10 years old.

2. He studied at night school.

3. A device that improved steam boiler furnaces to make them heat houses better. A telephone transmitter to improve the quality and distance of the sound sent. A set of tracks for motor cars to run on in amusement parks. A railway and telegraphy system used to communicate messages from one train to another. An overhead electric system to power trains. The third rail – a device which runs alongside a rail track to provide trains with electrical power. An incubator.

4. Over 35 patents for various electromechanical devices.

5. Thomas Edison and Phelps. He went there to be legally declared as the true inventor of various electrical devices.

6. Granville T. Woods won the court cases.

7. Thomas Edison and Phelps invited Granville T. Woods to join their company. Woods declined and decided to set up the Woods' Electrical Company with his brother Lyates Woods.

8. In 1974 the Governor of Ohio proclaimed Granville T. Woods as one of the greatest electricians in the world.

Dr. Mae C. Jemison

1. October 17th 1956 in Decatur, Alabama.

2. 3. BSc in Chemical Engineering, BA in African and Afro American studies, doctorate degree in Medicine.

3. Sierra Leone and Liberia in West Africa and Cambodia.

4. The Earth We Share promotes critical thinking and problem-solving skills. The Jemison Group Inc. concentrates on making science and technology work in everyday life. The Jemison Institute for Advancing Technology in Developing Countries promotes sustainable development.

5. Dr. Jemison is in the National Women's Hall of Fame, the National Medical Association Hall of Fame and has been awarded many honorary doctorates. She was also awarded The Essence Science and Technology Award, the Kilby Science Award.

6. Yes. Endeavor, 1992.

7. No, she left in March 1993.

8. 'Sustainable development' means to apply methods that improve the quality of human life such that future generations can grow and prosper.

INVENTOR SCIENTIST HISTORICAL FIGURE ANSWERS GLOSSARY TIMELINE

Answers

Elijah McCoy

1. May 2nd 1843 in Colchester, Ontario Canada.

2. Their parents wanted to give them the privilege to learn to read and write, which they would not have had, had they stayed in the USA and lived as slaves.

3. Mechanical Engineering.

4. 1870, the Elijah McCoy Manufacturing Company, Detroit, Michigan.

5. He wanted to work on a solution to automatically oil industrial machinery which would grind to a halt when the parts needed oiling.

6. Drip cup for oiling factory machinery, lubricator cup for railroads, ironing table and a lawn sprinkler. Over 50.

Jan Ernst Matzeliger

1. 1852 in Suriname.

2. He invented a machine that made shoe making process more efficient. It allowed many people to be able to afford to buy shoes. March 20th 1883.

3. He became a seaman. He sailed to the Far East.

4. Yes. Even though slavery had ended, many whites did not respect blacks enough to employ them.

5. They laughed at him.

6. Matzeliger's method was 6 to 14 times faster (300/50 = 6, 700/50 = 14) than the other lasting methods of the time.

7. No. He ended up a very poor man.

8. A postage stamp was printed in his honour in 1992.

Dr. Ernest Everett Just

1. South Carolina, USA, August 14th 1883. Charles Frazier and Mary Matthews Just.

2. He completed a 4-year course of study in 3 years.

3. Botany, Sociology and History.

4. 1907.

5. He was the only one to graduate as a magna cum laude or with a distinction.

6. A Doctor of Philosophy magna cum laude in Experimental Embryology.

7. He studied and researched a number of related subject areas such as egg fertilisation and cells.

8. He was awarded the Springarn Medal from the National Association for the Advancement of Coloured Peoples (NAACP) for his contribution to science and his race. He was the first African American vice-president of the American Society of Zoologists. He published many articles on his subject area.

Garrett A. Morgan

1. March 4th 1877. He had an elementary education.

2. He invented a belt fastener for sewing machines. He was a teenager

3. It is an official document used to prove that a person has invented something.

4. Gas mask. 1912.

5. July 4th 1916 in Ohio. An explosion occurred in a tunnel where over 30 men were trapped with no hope of rescue because of the smoke. Garrett and Frank Morgan rescued the men using Garrett's gas mask. This invention was used in fire departments, mining companies and by the US army during World War I.

6. Hair straightening cream in 1912 and a three-colour traffic signalling system in 1923.

NOTES

Glossary

Of Words And Terms Used

A

ABOLITION **means to ban or make illegal a particular behaviour or practice.**

ABSENT **means not being in a place where you are expected to be.**

ADVANCE **means to go forward, or to improve a method of doing something.**

ADVERTISEMENTS **are public announcements in the form of words and or pictures that are used to sell products and services by promoting specific images. For example, a person might purchase a car, because he/she was attracted to the way the people looked in the advertisement for that car.**

ALMANAC **is a book that includes information about the weather, planets, stars, calendars, the moon, medical remedies, poems and articles.**

ALLIANCE **is when two or more groups or countries come together or unite for a common purpose, which could be to fight a war.**

AMAZEMENT **means to be surprised or fascinated by something. As a child Benjamin Banneker gazed in amazement at the stars.**

AMUSEMENT **is something that is fun or makes you laugh.**

ANATOMY **is the science of the structure of the body.**

ARCHAEOLOGY **is the study of ancient or old cultures and people using their remains, which could be bones and ruins of temples, houses and other buildings.**

ASSESSES **means to carry out tests to find out the value or importance of something.**

ASTRONAUT **is a person who is trained to travel in space.**

ASTRONOMY **is a scientific study of the stars, planets and their behaviour.**

B

BEFRIENDED **means to make friends with a person.**

BIOLOGY **is the study of living organisms such as humans, plants and animals.**

BIOMEDICAL ENGINEERING **is a branch of study that looks at ways of producing machinery to improve the health of humans, plants and animals.**

BODIES **are the entire physical structure of animals, humans or the stars and planets usually referred to as** heavenly bodies**.**

BOTANY **is the study of plants.**

C

CATALYTIC CONVERTER is a device that chemically changes the fuel in the exhaust of a vehicle after COMBUSTION to cause the EMISSION of cleaner air. A catalyst is a chemical that can transform and speed up another chemical without changing its properties.

CARBON DIOXIDE is a gas with no colour, or smell that is exhaled or breathed out by animals and humans and breathed in by plants to produce starch. When plants are burned, carbon dioxide is also released.

CELLULAR means to do with the cells, which are the building blocks for humans, plants and animals.

CHEMISTRY is the study of the contents of substances and how they react to each other.

CIRCUMSTANCES are the conditions that affect a person. If a person cannot read, this circumstance could hinder him/her from enjoying a good book.

COLLEAGUES are people who you work or study with.

COMBUSTION is the process of combining substances with OXYGEN to produce heat, which takes the form of hot air, smoke or fire.

COMMUNICATE means to make your thoughts or feelings known to someone else. This could be by talking, painting, singing, drumming or sending other signals. Animals communicate with each other as well as with humans.

COMPASSIONATE means to be caring and thoughtful of other people's opinions and suffering. A compassionate person might help a less FORTUNATE person by donating some money, books or clothes to them.

COMPLETED means to finish a task.

COMPUTER is a machine that stores data or information. This data could be letters, sounds, numbers or pictures. To compute means to calculate. Therefore, a computer calculates how to store and retrieve or view data.

CONCEPTS are ideas. To understand a concept you must be able to describe it in your own words. Do you understand the concept of PHOTOSYNTHESIS?

CONSULTANT is a person who is skilled in a particular area and gives other people advice based on his/her KNOWLEDGE and EXPERIENCE.

CONSUMPTION is to devour or use up.

CONTESTING is to dispute or disagree with someone usually in a court.

CONTRIBUTION means to give, this could come in the form of research, money, or time. Dr. Ernest Everett Just contributed to the study of EMBRYOLOGY by conducting RESEARCH.

CULTURE is the ideas, art, customs, fashion, beliefs, language and practices of a group of people or society.

CURRICULUM is an outline or plan of a course such the General Certificate of Secondary Education (GCSE).

D

DEGREE is an award given by a university after a student has successfully completed period of studying.

DETERMINATION is when a person decides that no matter how hard the task or piece of work that they have to do is, they are not going to give up,.

DEVICE is a machine or tool that is used for a specific task. A device can be as small as a microchip in a computer or as large as a washing machine.

DIESEL is a FUEL produced by heating PETROLEUM and collecting the gas or vapour.

DILIGENT means careful and hardworking.

DISTINCTION a special mark, like an A★.

DIRECTOR is a person who runs or controls a business or an organisation.

DRAFTING means to plan, sketch or draw something.

INVENTOR

SCIENTIST

HISTORICAL FIGURE

ANSWERS

GLOSSARY

TIMELINE

Glossary

E

ECOCHARGER **is a device invented by Ron Headley in 1985. The Ecocharger prevents cars from polluting the environment by altering the chemical properties of the** FUEL **in the engine of a vehicle before** COMBUSTION **occurs.**

EDUCATION **is the process of learning. This may take place at home, at school, at college, at work or through experiencing life.**

ELECTROMECHANICAL **refers to a machine or** DEVICE **that uses electricity for movement, power, or speed.**

ELEMENTARY **means simple, straightforward and not too difficult.**

EMBRYO **is unborn human or animal in its early stages of development.**

EMBRYOLOGY **is the study of early development of humans or animals in the** WOMB **or in an egg.**

EMINENT **means well-known or respected.**

EMISSION **is the excretion or giving out of** FUEL**, light or smell.**

ENDEAVOUR **means to try to do something.**

ENGINEERING **is a profession that applies scientific principles to the design and construction of machines such as cars, trains, ships and computers.**

ENTREPRENEUR **is a person who tries to make money or to profit from his/her** INITIATIVE**.**

EXCEL **to be very good, outstanding or excellent at something.**

EXPERIENCE **is something that happens to a person. We learn by our life experiences.**

EXPERIENTIAL **means to learn by** EXPERIENCE **or by doing something.**

EXPERIMENT **is a test that is carried out to prove or disprove a theory. For example Madame C.J Walker experimented with hair growing solutions to test if by using them her hair would really grow.**

EXPLORATION **means to go somewhere to find out new facts about how people live or the environment.** ASTRONAUTS **regularly go on** SPACE **explorations.**

F

FERTILISATION **is the process where the male and female sex cells in humans, plants and animals join together to reproduce, or create new life.**

FOCUS **means to pay special attention to something. Dr. Mae C. Jemison decided to focus her career on** BIOMEDICAL ENGINEERING**.**

FOETUS **is a human or an animal in the later stages of development.**

FORMAL **means the expected way of doing things or behaving at particular occasions. Benjamin Banneker had no formal qualifications, meaning he did not have the expected documents to prove his knowledge.**

FORTUNATE **means lucky. Elijah McCoy was fortunate to be given the** OPPORTUNITY **to get an** EDUCATION**.**

FUEL **is a substance that is burned either to produce heat, power or speed.**

G

GRADUATE **means to pass or** COMPLETE **a course of study for example,** DEGREE.

H

HIRE **means to pay to borrow something like a car or a piece of machinery.**

HISTORY **is a record of events that took place in the past.**

HONOUR **means to have the** RESPECT **and privilege because of the work that a person has done.**

HONORARY **means some has been given an award or title for the work they have done.**

Dr. Jemison has received many honorary doctorates for the work that she has done.

I

ILLEGAL **means not keeping with the laws of the country where you live.**

ILLUSION **is an object or a thing that appears to be so real that you think you can touch it or see it, but when you go to feel it or look closer, it is not what it appears to be.**

ILLUSTRATE **means to explain or show something by using examples such as picture, a story or by something that has happened to you.**

INCUBATOR **is a heated structure to nurture a baby who was born before the 9-month gestation or the expected growth period for an embryo to develop into a child.**

INDUSTRIAL **means used in the** MANUFACTURING **of goods.**

INITIATIVE **means to use your mind to come up with solutions independently or without being asked.**

INNOVATION **is a new way of doing things. An innovation could be an improvement on an existing invention.**

INSTITUTIONS **are large organisations such as banks, churches, and schools.**

'INSTIL PRIDE' **means to make someone feel good about who they are.**

INTERNET **is a** NETWORK **of computers that store information in words, pictures and sound and are connected together allowing people to** COMMUNICATE**. When a person logs on to the Internet, they do so using the telephone line and a modem. Once connected, they can surf the information stored on the many computers using a program called the World Wide Web (www). This program allows a person to visit and search for information on different computers in different countries, at the touch of a button.**

INTRIGUED **means to be very interested in something.**

K

KNOWLEDGE **is our understanding of facts about the world in which we live.**

INVENTOR

SCIENTIST

HISTORICAL FIGURE

ANSWERS

GLOSSARY

TIMELINE

Glossary

L

LATHE MACHINE is a DEVICE that holds pieces of wood or metal whilst a person works on them.

LEGACY means that after a person dies, they are remembered for what they did when they were alive. Their EXPERIENCES can be used as examples of how the people who are still alive should behave.

M

MAGNA CUM LAUDE this means to COMPLETE a DEGREE, with such good grades that you are awarded a distinction.

MAINTENANCE means to keep in good working order. To maintain a car, it needs to be serviced.

MANUFACTURING means to make products on a large scale, usually in a factory.

MECHANICAL DEVICES are parts or machines that perform a specific function. Elijah McCoy's DRIP CUP is an example of a mechanical device.

MEDICINE is a substance used to treat a disease. When a person studies Medicine they learn how to treat, prevent and cure diseases. They also learn how to find out or diagnose a person as being infected with a particular disease.

MILLIONAIRE is a person who owns money or possessions that add up to the value of a million units or more in the currency of the country where they live. If they live in England that would be a million pounds, in Ghana a million Cedis, in America a million dollars.

MONOGRAPH is a study of one particular section or subject area.

N

NASA is the National Aeronautical Space Administration organisation in the USA.

NATIONAL means to do with a country or nation.

NEGATIVE means to think, feel bad or say bad things about a thing, event or a person. It is the opposite of POSITIVE.

NETWORK is a way to connect people, machines or systems such as buses and trains so that they can COMMUNICATE.

NICKNAME is a name that friends and family use for a person. Benjamin Banneker's neighbours called him "the stargazer".

O

OPERATOR is a person who knows how to work a DEVICE. For example a switchboard operator.

OPPORTUNITY means to be given the chance to do something.

OXYGEN is a gas with no colour or smell that all living things need to survive. It is produced during PHOTOSYNTHESIS.

P

PASSIONATE **to be really enthusiastic or eager about someone or something. Benjamin Banneker was passionate about** ASTRONOMY.

PATENT **is an official document used to prove that a person has invented or is allowed to sell a product.**

PERSONNEL **is another word for people. It normally refers to people who work for the same company.**

PETROL **is a refined oil that is produced from** PETROLEUM **and is used in the internal** COMBUSTION **engines of vehicles such as cars, lorries, and buses.**

PETROLEUM **is a crude or pure** FUEL **found deep in the earth.**

PHILOSOPHY **is the study of ideas or** CONCEPTS.

PHOTOSYNTHESIS **takes place in the leaves of plants. It is a chemical reaction to light from the sun,** CARBON DIOXIDE **from the air and water from the soil, which is combined to make starch for storage, energy, or to produce proteins, necessary for growth and** OXYGEN.

PHYSIOLOGY **is the science of understanding how humans, plants and animals function.**

PIONEER **means the first one to do something. Dr. Daniel Hale Williams was a pioneer because he performed the first open-heart surgery in 1893.**

POLITICS **is a person's ideas and thoughts about how a country or system should be governed or run and who should have the power in that government or system.**

POSSESS **means to own something.**

POSITIVE **means to think, feel good, or say good things about a thing, an event, or a person. It is the opposite of** NEGATIVE.

PRINCIPLES **are a set of rules guiding behaviour, or how something works.**

PROSPER **means to be rich or successful.**

R

RACE **is a group of people who share the same ancestry and other attributes such as skin colour, eye colour, hair texture, body shape that distinguish them from another group people.**

RESEARCH **means to study about a particular topic or a group of topics. This involves reading books, articles, journals on the subject conducting interviews, asking questions and writing a report or a thesis on the subject.**

RESIGNED **is when a person decides that they no longer wish to work for a company.**

RESPECT **means to admire or look up to someone because of who they are, what they have done or because they are older and more** EXPERIENCED **than you are. You should also admire yourself for the things that you have achieved. Remember always to treat others as you would like to be treated.**

RIGOROUS **means strict and well controlled. Madame C.J Walker carried out rigorous tests before she started to sell her products.**

INVENTOR

SCIENTIST

HISTORICAL FIGURE

ANSWERS

GLOSSARY

TIMELINE

Glossary

S

SCIENCE is the application of specific methods to study things or behaviour that occur in nature or people.

SEGREGATED means to divide or separate, keep one group of people away from the rest of society who make up the majority.

SHARECROPPER is a person who rents land (tenant) from another person (landlord) for the purposes of farming, and keeps a share of the crops produced from the farm while the remainder goes to the landlord as rent for the land.

SHUTTLE is a vehicle that travels a long distance in a short space of time.

SLAVERY means to buy or sell another human being and have total control over that person's life. A slave works for a slave owner without pay.

SOCIOLOGY is the study of human groups or societies.

SOLAR ECLIPSE occurs when the new moon passes between the earth and the sun and partially or totally blocks out the light from the sun. A lunar eclipse occurs when the moon moves into the shadow of the earth.

SPACE is the region of the universe outside of the earth's atmosphere.

SURGERY means when a person's body is cut open to treat a part that is diseased.

SURVEYOR is a person who examines the condition of a piece of property or land and/or measures and maps out where to place buildings or structures.

'SUSTAINABLE DEVELOPMENT' means to apply methods that improve the quality of human life now, such that future generations can grow and prosper.

T

TECHNOLOGY means to use science, or machines to make money or to create an industry. Technological is something relating to technology for a example the mobile phone industry is a technological advancement in telecommunications.

TELECOMMUNICATIONS means to COMMUNICATE using the television, radio, satellite, telephone and the INTERNET.

TELEGRAPHY was a system used to communicate messages over long distances using a telegraph cable.

THESIS is a written work completed for a DEGREE.

TM means Trademark, which is a mark to indicate that a symbol, title or label belongs to a specific person.

TREATMENT is to take care of or heal a person and make them well again.

U

UNDERGROUND RAILROAD is a term used to describe a large network of people who helped slaves in the Southern States in America to escape to The Northern States or Canada where they would be free.

V

VIRUS is a small organism that takes over the nucleus, which is the control centre of a cell, causing that cell to behave abnormally. When a cell is abnormal, the body is in a diseased state. Examples of viruses are, chickenpox, measles, flu, and rubella.

W

WOMB is a hollow organ in female animals and humans where babies are conceived or made and developed.

WORLD WAR I (1914 - 1918). This war occurred as a result of a disagreement between Germany, Austria, Hungary who had formed an alliance with France and Russia. Britain went to war after Germany invaded Belgium.

WORLD WAR II (1939 - 1945). This war was instigated by Adolph Hitler who came to power in 1933 and wanted to restore Germany's position as a world power after its defeat in World War I and invaded Poland. Britain and France formed an alliance and went to war with Germany.

Y

YELLOW FEVER is viral disease carried by mosquitoes. The symptoms of yellow fever begin to appear 9-12 days after receiving bite from a mosquito carrier. The VIRUS damages the liver and causes a yellowish bile pigment to gather in the skin. Other symptoms of the disease are fever, headaches, dizziness and muscle ache.

Z

ZOOLOGIST is a person who studies animals.

INVENTOR

SCIENTIST

HISTORICAL FIGURE

ANSWERS

GLOSSARY

TIMELINE

Timeline
Of Scientists, Inventors & Inventions

1731	Inventor, astronomer Benjamin Banneker is born in Maryland, USA.
1771	Benjamin Banneker assists in the planning of Washington DC.
1792	Benjamin Banneker publishes his first almanac.
1806	Inventor, astronomer Benjamin Banneker dies.
1843	Inventor Elijah McCoy is born in Ontario, Canada.
1852	Inventor Jan Ernst Matzeliger is born in Guyana, South America.
1856	Inventor Granville T. Woods is born in Ohio, USA.
1867	Inventor and first African-American woman millionaire, Madame C.J Walker is born in the USA.
1870	Inventor Elijah McCoy sets up the Elijah McCoy Manufacturing Company in Detrioit, Michigan, USA.
1872	Elijah McCoy patents the lubricator cup for steam engines and the drip cup for factory machines.
1874	Elijah McCoy patents the steam lubricators.
1876	Elijah McCoy patents his steam cylinder lubricator.
1877	Inventor Garrett A. Morgan is born in Kentucky, USA.
1882	Elijah McCoy patents a lubricator.
1883	Biologist Dr. Ernest Everett Just is born in South Carolina, USA. Jan Ernst Matzeliger patents his shoe lasting machine.
1884	Granville T. Woods patents his telephone transmitter and his improvement to steam boiler furnaces.
1885	Elijah McCoy patents a lubricator.*
1887	Granville T. Woods patents a polarized relay. Granville T. Woods patents the induction telegraph system.
1888	Granville T. Woods patents an overhead electric system. Granville T. Woods patents a tunnel construction for electric railways. Granville T. Woods patents his galvanic battery.
1889	Hodge and Elijah McCoy patent the lubricator.* Inventor Jan Ernst Matzeliger dies in the USA.
1891	Granville T Woods patents the safety cut out for electric circuits. Granville T. Woods patents an electric railway system.

Timeline
Of Scientists, Inventors & Inventions

1892	Elijah McCoy patents a lubricator.*
1896	After his death, Jan Ernst Matzeliger earns a patent for a nailing machine.. Granville T. Woods patents a system for electrical distribution.
1898	Elijah McCoy patents an oil cup.
1899	After his death, Jan Ernst Matzeliger earns a patent for a mechanism for distributing tacks.
1903	Granville T. Woods patents an electric railway system.
1901	Granville T. Woods patents electric railway. Granville T. Woods patents regulating, controlling and electrical translating devices.
1905	Granville T. Woods patents a set of railway brakes. Madame C.J Walker patents her hair care products along with the straightening comb.
1910	Inventor Granville T. Woods dies.
1914	Dr. Ernest Everett Just receives Springarn medal for his pioneering research on fertilisation and cell division.
1919	Inventor Madame C.J Walker dies in the USA.
1923	Garrett A. Morgan patents the traffic signalling system.
1929	Inventor Elijah McCoy dies.
1930	Pioneering biologist Dr. Ernest Everett Just becomes the first African American vice president of the American Society of Zoologists.
1939	Inventor, cricketer Ron Headley is born in Kingston Jamaica.
1941	Biologist Dr. Ernest Everett Just dies.
1956	Astronaut, Dr. Mae C. Jemison is born in Alabama, USA.
1963	Inventor Garrett A. Morgan dies.
1974	The governor of Ohio, USA issues a proclamation to recognise inventor Granville T. Woods as one of the greatest electricians in the world.
1985	Inventor, cricketer Ron Headley patents his Ecocharger™ device for reducing fuel emission from diesel cars.
1988	Dr. Mae C. Jemison receives the Essence Science and Technology award.
1992	Dr. Mae C. Jemison becomes the first African American woman in space.

* An improvement to a previous patent

INVENTOR

SCIENTIST

HISTORICAL FIGURE

ANSWERS

GLOSSARY

TIMELINE

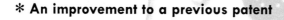

1. **Black Africa - The Economic and Cultural Basis for a Federated State**
   C.A. DIOP, Lawrence Hill & Co 1978
   ISBN: 0-88208-096-2

2. **Black Apollo of Science - The Life of Ernest Just**
   K.R. Manning, OXFORD UNIVERSITY PRESS, NEW YORK
   ISBN: 0-19-503299-3

3. **Black Inventors from Africa to America**
   C.R. Gibbs, Three Dimensional Publishing, 1995
   ISBN: 1-877835-87-0

4. **Black Scientists of America**
   R.X. Donovan, National Book Company, 1990
   ISBN: 0-89420-265-0

5. **Blacks in Science - Ancient and Modern**
   edited by Ivan Van Sertima, Journal of African Civilisation Ltd, Inc, 1983
   ISBN: 0-87855-941-8

6. **Collins Gem English Learners Dictionary**
   1980
   ISBN: 0-00-458336-1

7. **Geddes & Grosset Dictionary of Science**
   1992
   ISBN: 1-85534-099-2

8. **Our Story**
   edited by Akyaaba- Sebo and Ansel Wong, LSPU/LBH 1988,
   ISBN: 1-8700 13 11-1